PARSON
McFRIGHT

PARSON McFRIGHT

SHORT STORIES FOR HARRIED CHURCHMEN

by Allen Whitman

Illustrated by
Dorothy Messenger

AUGSBURG PUBLISHING HOUSE
MINNEAPOLIS, MINNESOTA

PARSON McFRIGHT

Copyright © 1967 Augsburg Publishing, House

Library of Congress Catalog Card No. 67-25370

Manufactured in the United States of America

Dedication

To Robert Johnson,
the midwife of the material.

With many thanks to Aldythe Johnson,
Mimi Borden, and Ernie Campbell
for their criticism and assistance.

Introduction

There was a day when the local clergyman was called the "parson" because he was one of the best-educated and most respected "persons" in his community, but that day is long past. Today a pastor is often no better educated than many men and women in his parish. Many parishioners, in fact, will even surpass him both in academic training and native intelligence. As a result, a pastor today is no longer respected automatically; instead, he must earn his respect on an equal footing with his parishioners. He must struggle to become a respected person, fighting an inner battle which outsiders can appreciate but which Christians can really know and understand.

Communities still desperately need parsons, but the kind of parson they need must be willing to grow as a person. He must first demonstrate to his parishioners a transparent relationship to the living Christ he has come to know in the Bible and in encounters in real life. But he cannot be only a leader; he must also be open to the people in his parish—both in the church and outside of it—who just as truly as he demonstrate the truth of Christ in their lives. By both leading others and learning from others he will deserve the respect traditionally due to a "parson," and his example can also help others to become the persons God has created them to be.

Parson McFright may be such a person; at least he is openly struggling with what God is calling him to do and to be.

Contents

Chapter I

Watch and Pray

Parson McFright was in a serious dilemma. Should he —or should he not—pray for the success of the Tri-City Canaries, a long-suffering baseball club if there ever was one?

This was not the first time this particular problem had confronted him. In seminary, debates had raged between the backers of Southern Methodist and Notre Dame in football. Did the outcome of Saturday afternoon's game indicate that the prayers of the Protestants were more effective than those of the Roman Catholics, or was it the other way around? Each side would gleefully remind the other that intercessions seemed somehow more effective when your team had linemen weighing two-fifty and backs who could run the hundred in less than ten seconds.

Still, his problem remained: either prayer is effective or ineffective. Should one dare to pray for a school or home team in an athletic event; if he did, how could he do it without being sacrilegiously partisan and narrowminded?

Parson McFright carried a portable transistor radio with him with the faithfulness of a teen-age Beatles fan and with the stealth of a C.I.A. agent. Uppermost in his mind was the fantastic rise of the inept Canaries, who this year were making an unexpected bid for the pennant. Each cliff-hanger contest—when the outcome hung in the balance until the last out—seemed to call for the intercessions of the saints, and Parson McFright had never been one to fall down on the job. He knew there were members of the Christian Athletes' Association and the Youth for Christ movement on the opposing pitching staffs, but an all-out spiritual effort still seemed to be in order. After all, the Canaries hadn't been in the pennant scramble since before World War I! The right time for prayer had obviously come, and it was only with great restraint that Parson McFright held back his verbal appeals to the Heavenly Umpire as unworthy of a man of the cloth.

He could even justify intercession theologically. Why shouldn't God be as interested in the outcome of the contest between the Canaries and the Bulldogs as he had been in the Israelites and the Philistines? Was it not a simple matter of degree? Are not the hairs on one's head numbered and does not a sparrow fall but God knoweth it altogether? Is not the real heresy of our age the fact that many people, even practicing Christians, never realize that God is present everywhere and is concerned with our every-day labor? And every Canary ballplayer was working for his living, just like the laborer in the stockyard, the corporation executive, or the struggling pastor with his flock. Such were Parson McFright's musings during his more ecstatic moments.

In moments of depression—generally after the Canaries had thrown one away in the ninth—Parson McFright would condemn baseball as unworthy of either his or God's serious attention. At such times it seemed like a modern version of the Roman games in which the spiritual lives of countless millions were placed in jeopardy. Not only did baseball encourage a senseless waste of time and energy, but the success or failure of an individual team became more important than the coming of God's kingdom into the world.

Such being the conscious condition of the Rev. Parson McFright, it was not surprising that during the wee, small hours one morning he chanced to have a dream.

He was in the ball park, and it was filled with wildly cheering fans. It was the last half of the ninth inning and the Canaries were on the field, protecting a shaky one-run lead. The bases were loaded with the gray uniforms of the hated Bulldogs. The Canaries had made a frantic call to the bullpen for relief pitcher Stingy O'Toole, who had an uncanny ability to get the opposition out for one or two innings.

As usual, Parson McFright was hysterically beside himself, calling the manager Raca—"Thou fool"—for not sending in O'Toole long before this. Such had been the parson's inner turmoil that only now, for the first time, he noticed the umpire behind the plate. The umpire was dressed in the usual dark suit with the bulging chest protector and pulled-down cap, but he seemed unusually at ease as he watched O'Toole throw in his warm-up pitches, and his voice had a rich, melodious quality as he hollered out, "Play ball!" What especially attracted Parson McFright's attention was not just the way the umpire acted, nor was it his voice with its clear tone. What Parson McFright saw with astounding clarity were the umpire's eyes, eyes which gave the official a strangely familiar look.

Parson McFright's attention, though, was soon drawn back to the game as O'Toole toed the rubber and the Bulldog runners led off dancing down the basepaths. O'Toole wound up and threw. "Strike one." The clear voice of the umpire seemed to dominate even the screaming of the fans. O'Toole took a little rosin, glanced over at first and third, hardly looked at the catcher's sign— knew what he was going to throw anyway—and gave the Bulldog batter his famous forkball. The batter swung. Parson McFright's heart was in his throat as he watched the ball bounce between a diving third baseman and shortstop and into left field. One run scored. The runner from second made the turn from third and headed for the plate. With his bare hand the Canary left fielder made a brilliant pickup and with one motion threw the ball to the waiting

catcher at the plate. The runner dove. Dust rose in the
air. The crowd waited—it seemed like eternity—for the
umpire's decision. "Safe!" The clear, melodious voice of the
umpire twisted an invisible knife in the heart of every
Canary fan.

"Robber!" screamed Parson McFright from his privileged
position on the field. Oh, why had that idiotic manager not
called in O'Toole earlier? "We've lost," murmured Parson
McFright unbelievingly, "and that lousy manager is all to
blame!"

Then Parson McFright saw that the umpire, instead of
going off the field, was walking directly toward him. There
was something awesome about the way he looked, the quick-
ness of his stride and the direction of his piercing eyes made
Parson McFright suddenly aware that the umpire wanted a
personal word with him. There was a vague prickling of
fear along Parson McFright's spine. The hair on his scalp
seemed to rise. He thought for an instant that the world
around him might cave in. The hands of the umpire, now
on top of him, moved over him like a weird kind of bless-
ing. "You're safe!" the voice cried in that melodious way.

Parson McFright awoke bathed in sweat as though he'd
been playing on the field. It was as if he had just experienced as a living, concrete reality who it is that judges the
living and the dead.

In a strange and painful way he now knew the answer to
his conflict over prayer. For when a man is emotionally in-

volved in any sport, and God is present as God is, prayer rises as naturally as mist before the dawn. But God forgive the man who tries to take the part of God in any of life's games.

Not Parson McFright's prayers but his attitudes were questioned and found wanting this memorable might.

Chapter II

A Demonstration

The apparent serenity of Parson McFright's parish was rudely shattered the day the newspapers and television showed him marching in a peaceful demonstration against an unwritten housing restriction in a wealthy section of his city.

Parson McFright had never been active in any social-action movement before. His involvement had arisen almost unintentionally when a parishioner showed him evidence concerning a verbal covenant among homeowners in the fashionable "Garden" area of Tri-City. Parson McFright had gone with his problem to a clerical colleague who was up to his ears in political affairs, and before he had fully realized what was happening, a march was on, reporters had been called and there he was on the evening news and on the front pages of the morning papers.

The theological expressions used by some of his most upstanding communicants, upon viewing Parson McFright's somewhat troubled face on the before-bedtime telecast, clearly denied that such concepts were no longer being used.

"My gawd, isn't that McFright?" (uttered by the parish treasurer) was the least of these remarks.

Since some fifteen fairly substantial, contributing communicants lived in the Garden section, Parson McFright's public witness was not ignored. The best description of the telephone lines between certain close parishioners was "hot." Remarks varied from out-and-out shock that their pastor would dare act in such a manner to the indignant remark of Jeremy Blister, "A clergyman has no business parading up and down the street about something that is none of his business. What do we pay him for?" On the other hand, a few of McFright's non-churchgoing neighbors made their way over to his lawn to tell him that he had a lot of "guts," and a total stranger pressed his hand in the drugstore in a sincere expression of agreement and thanks.

By the evening of the second day, however, the considerable number of phone calls which had been made to the wardens and members of the vestry indicated that storm warnings were in the air. "I know those covenants weren't exactly kosher," expostulated a long-time member of St. Hilary, "but we didn't call a man to represent our church by making a public spectacle of himself."

"Listen, Tracey," exploded one Garden-view homeowner to the senior warden, "if you guys don't bring McFright down a peg on this, I'll cancel my pledge just like that and transfer to St. Swithuns."

Sunday's attendance made people think of Easter on a

sunny April day. There were those people who were there because they suspected fireworks either from the pulpit or the pew. There were those who came to gather support for a "chastise McFright movement." There were those who came because for once they respected McFright. There were even those who came to worship God at the altar. The combination kept the ushers busy setting up chairs, until midway through each service.

Writing a sermon had been a difficult battle for the now apprehensive Parson McFright. His first reaction had been to ignore the episode altogether, but unfortunately, the Old Testament lessons seemed to reek with God's demand for justice, and the New Testament said that he who doth not take up his cross and follow me is not worthy of me. "For heaven's sake, go easy Sunday," Tracey, the senior warden, had cautiously advised. "I'm really waiting to hear you Sunday," murmured one lady whom McFright respected, as he passed her on a crowded street. Deep in his heart Parson McFright knew he had an opportunity to say something important. And yet, gnawing at his vitals was the dark suspicion that his life and work as the priest of this parish was directly on the line.

The singing that morning was rather listless. The congregation mouthed the responses and had the usual glazed expression while the scripture lesson was being read. "Do not think that I have come to bring peace on earth; I have not come to bring peace but a sword," the layreader read in stentorian tones, "and he who does not take his cross and follow me is not worthy of me. He who finds his life will lose it, and he who loses his life for my sake will find it." But when Parson McFright climbed into the pulpit the attention he had was positively awesome.

McFright had experimented with a few lines that might have eased the tension, such as "A funny thing happened to me on the way to the Garden . . . ," but by the grace of God he had discarded each of them as his opening. He began where he was.

"God has rarely demanded courage of me as a Christian," he started. "I have discovered this week that it does not take much courage to protest a wrong which other people are committing, but that it does take courage to stand up before you now and speak honestly without fear of the consequences.

"Many of you saw me doing something last week that frankly I have never felt moved to do before. I wore my clericals as a Christian pastor only because I found it incongruous that Christians meet together at the altar on Sunday regardless of race and color, and then set up barriers so they cannot meet in their neighborhoods on the same basis. This to me is as illogical for Christians as the cliquish behavior St. Paul complains about in the second chapter of First Corinthians.

"I also walked in protest as a citizen of this country. It appeared to me manifestly unjust that certain citizens, re-

gardless of their church affiliation, should be excluded from living in one neighborhood by an agreement no one dared to admit in the broad light of day.

"Many of you may be thinking that this past week your pastor acted in a peculiarly self-righteous way. It is so easy, especially as a clergyman, to act in a manner which appears 'holier than thou.' But I discovered something in myself these past days which has shattered that illusion for me. Recently I have noticed a timidity within me, one which probably has always existed. This timidity might have kept me from demonstrating if the issue had not been so blatantly clear, and this timidity made me wish to dodge the issue this morning. In short, I discovered in myself the play-acting hypocrite, who deserved the scathing words of our Lord, 'a white-washed tomb,' with a round collar. I do trust that this morning we may break bread together as brothers in Christ, as fellow sinners, whatever our race or whatever our color. Let us accept God's forgiveness and God's strength to live in the world with the same grace that we find together at the Lord's altar."

There were those in church that Sunday who were sincerely moved by Parson McFright's words. Many didn't really understand them and were let down that there were no pyrotechnics or communicants stomping out the door. Several, like Jeremy Blister, were not even listening. Jeremy was going over in his mind the appropriate words to use as he gave the pastor his letter of resignation at the door. He wanted to say the most effective thing possible, and with as many people as possible within earshot. But each time he tried out an expression such as "You've gone too far for me, McFright" the words seemed somehow inappropriate. The communion service had made him feel more and more uncomfortable; for the first time in his life he had the strange feeling that he didn't belong. To add to his plight, there were now many at the door warmly shaking McFright's hand, even though many of them, he was sure, didn't agree with the action any more than he. So finally Jeremy merely stuck the letter into Parson McFright's outstretched hand and walked hastily by without so much as a grunt. McFright absentmindedly placed the letter in his pocket; his mind was on more immediate things.

When all had left, Parson McFright sat at his desk and wiped his brow. No one, not one person, had reprimanded him in any way. No one had walked out. A few people had probably neglected to make their communions that morning, although the church had been extremely full. On the way home he mailed some letters at the mailbox and arrived home half expecting a phone call from certain members of his flock. None came.

The next day Jeremy Blister was surprised to receive the unopened letter he had handed to Parson McFright returned for postage and insufficient address. "I hate that guy's guts," he muttered, but he had nothing more to say.

Chapter III

The Thief in the Night

Parson McFright awoke with a start. He was certain he had heard a noise in the living room below. Despite anything he could do about it, his heart was pounding. Had he imagined it? No, the sound was unmistakable. Someone was moving around downstairs. No doubt about it.

A series of questions flashed through his mind in rapid succession. Was it one of his children? Why hadn't the dog barked? Why would anyone wish to break into a parsonage of all places? Would the intruder be armed? Had he offended anyone? Was someone out to get him?

Cautiously, he approached the stairway. Sure enough, a flashlight beam was visible, circling this way and that. The parson swallowed hard. He wanted to cry out, "Who's there?" but the words seemed to stick in his throat.

Instead, with a kind of nightmarish feeling, he began to walk slowly down the stairs. The light went out. The parson's hand vainly fumbled for the light switch. Somehow it wasn't where it was supposed to be. He reached the lower floor and turned. Sure enough, silhouetted against the window was a human form.

24

"Who's there?" began the parson in a tense voice. "Who . . . what do you mean by breaking in like this?"

"I didn't break in," was the resonant reply.

"I closed the windows myself and locked all the doors." The parson's tremulous voice carried a touch of anger. "You're a liar as well as a thief."

"The two go together," replied the stranger mildly.

"Well, what do you want?" The parson's hoarse whisper almost echoed in the room. "Money?"

"No."

"See here, if you are planning to hurt any of my family it will be over my dead body."

"I do not wish to harm your family," said the hidden figure.

"What do you want then?"

"You." The word seemed to penetrate every cell and pore in the parson's terrified body. He couldn't see the man but it was obvious he was face to face with a "hired gun."

"Are you sure . . .? I'm Parson McFright . . . are you sure [weakly] you want me?"

"You." There was a note of finality in the word.

"Before you kill me, then, would you mind telling me why I'm being shot down?"

"I'm not here to kill you," said the voice. "I'm here to raise you up."

"Raise me up . . .?" There was an unearthly silence. The parson felt his knees about to give way. He had no means of knowing whether he was about to receive the *coup de grace* or whether he was being teased within an inch of his frightened life.

"Last night you prayed for help. You needn't be afraid."

"Do you mind if I put on the light?" asked the parson.

"I prefer the dark," said the stranger. "But sit down if you wish."

The parson sank into one of his living room chairs. "How can I be sure you aren't pulling my leg?"

"You can't," replied the stranger evenly, "but I am here to raise you up and I do prefer the dark.

The parson pondered these words in silence.

"Last night you asked for guidance and strength," the visitor continued. He left the statement hanging.

"I know. I'm doing such a miserable job with my church."

"Whose church?"

"I mean the Lord's church . . . What I can't understand," pursued McFright, suddenly irritated, "is why you have to break in on me at night. I mean, aren't there some other ways of helping a guy like me?"

"To those who are of the light I must come in the dark, and to those of the dark I must come in the light," the stranger replied enigmatically.

"Will you try that again?" murmured the parson in a puzzled tone.

"You're a good man, a reasonable man," said the stranger, without a trace of annoyance. "You look for God in the orderly, the decent, the clean, the beautiful—the lovely, joyful aspects of life. It is your task to find yourself and God also in the irrational, the disorderly, the dirty, the evil—often the underside of life. That is why I come to you by night."

"You mean with another you would come by day?"

"Perhaps," reflected the stranger. "If one did not believe in goodness or had difficulty in accepting love, that might be the only way. The mystery is the same; only the approach is different."

"All right then," countered the parson, "I wanted advice and guidance to deal with these church people I've been sent to serve. What can I do with them? They don't think of themselves as 'Christians.' They're 'Americans,' 'lodge men,' 'college men,' or 'service-club men' before they're God's men. How do I change the image they carry in the street with them and in their homes? I've worked at this for years. I've preached, I've taught, I've begged, I've gotten angry with them. Frankly, it's too much for me; I'm just about through."

"That's why I'm here tonight," said the stranger in a comforting way. "I figured you didn't need advice so much as you needed *me*."

"You're probably right," admitted the Parson. "Boy, I really need something—or someone. But what about this job of mine? How do I go about it?"

"I'm here with you, am I not?" replied the voice. "There's

no reason why I can't be with them too. I'll be with them if
they really want me—*really* want me, as you did."

"But . . . how do I convince *them?* And to be honest, why
would they want an eerie experience like this? Why, I'm
still sweating, and I have goose-pimples all over me."

With a start the parson realized that the stranger was no
longer with him. He had simply disappeared. The parson
blinked his eyes. He was in the living room all right. He
switched on the light. No one was there. The dog was sleep-
ing peacefully in one corner. The windows were shut and
the doors locked. He was still sweating. Was it a dream?
Had he been walking in his sleep?

* * * *

"You certainly were restless, dear," the parson's wife told
him after morning coffee. "I had the feeling you were out
of bed half the night. Were you worried about something?
If you don't mind my saying so, you look a little white and
shaky."

"You would be too if you'd gone through what I went
through," said the parson grimly.

"Can you tell me about it?" His wife wanted to understand.

"Not right now, thanks," sighed the parson. "All I know
is that whatever it was, it was very real. Tell me," he continued, lifting his open Bible, "when it says in Scripture that
the Lord will come 'as a thief in the night,' what does that
mean to you?"

Chapter IV

Caesar

Years ago, Parson McFright had enjoyed the reputation of "Sky Pilot." Several times during the war he had been given the royal treatment on routine Navy flights to see if he could stand the gaff. Many chaplains had staggered out of the cockpit white and shattered, but Parson McFright, with the stomach of a surgeon and the balance of a gyroscope, had always stepped out beaming, thanking the flight officer for a delightful trip. Recently, however, this self-image of a modest superman in clerical habit had been greatly inhibited and it expressed itself only in the way Parson McFright drove his car. It wasn't that he was reckless or took wild chances, but his speed indicated that he was a man in a hurry or on important business.

Parson McFright rationalized his excessive speed on several counts. He wasn't going far over the limit, he would tell himself, and after all, he was on the Lord's business. Regulations were guides to better judgment, and his was the best. For years he got away with it, hardening his rationalization, even indicating that the Lord approved of his behavior.

Imagine Parson McFright's shock one day when he saw a policeman step out in front of him, raise his hand in a commanding gesture, order him to the side of the road, and inquire: "Sir, do you realize that you were going fifteen miles over the speed limit according to our radar system?"

There is much in the New Testament about honoring the authorities and the magistrates—rendering unto Caesar what is Caesar's. But Parson McFright had been operating above the law in this area for so long that a host of excuses immediately came into his head. "I'm sorry, officer, I was hurrying to make a hospital call," was the first excuse to cross his mind as he reached for his driver's license. Only he wasn't going in the right direction for the hospital. "But officer, I'm a priest" was his second thought as he realized that he was in a precarious and perhaps an embarrassing situation. He settled for charm instead.

"Gee, you're right." Parson McFright sounded surprised. "You know, I've never been caught before. I must have been thinking of something else." He hoped the officer would put him down as an absent-minded professor.

The officer was unimpressed. "I can't understand how a man in your position would risk the lives of others by the way he drives. You should set an example."

Parson McFright was stung where it hurt the most. In fact, he was tongue-tied for a second or two but then in desperation he kept up the same line.

"You're right, absolutely right. I just wasn't thinking."

To Parson McFright's horror the officer took out his pad and began to write.

"Are you giving me a ticket?" queried the now worried parson.

"Should you be treated differently than anyone else?" The words had a bite to them that twisted somewhere in Parson McFright's lower regions. "You were going more than ten miles over the limit, so you'll have to report to the judge. I hope this will be a good lesson for you."

The words were merciless. Parson McFright wanted to scream out, "Don't you know who I am?" but the words stuck in his throat.

The day of the court proceedings dawned dark and gloomy—at least in the eyes of Parson McFright. One little question had been gnawing at him for several days: Should he wear his clericals when he faced the judge, or should he appear only as a private citizen? If he wore his clericals, the court might have pity on him, but everyone there would see him disgracing the church by his presence. On the other hand, it seemed like a kind of subterfuge to come any other way except by publicly affirming his vocation and life. "After all," he thought morosely, "aren't all Christians—including clergy—guilty under the law, be it God's or man's?"

"Surely you aren't wearing your collar!" his wife cried when she saw he was about to leave. "What will the people in court think?"

Parson McFright winced. "I don't think that's as impor-

tant as what God thinks," he muttered. "Anyway, I've decided to be a clergyman come what may."

The Judge looked down at the red-faced parson. "You
are charged with driving forty-five miles an hour in a
thirty-mile zone. Have you anything you want to say?
Er . . . were there any extenuating circumstances that
you wish to tell the court?"

"No, Sir," replied McFright in a husky voice. "I've developed some bad driving habits through the years and was
just caught, I guess. I'm truly sorry about this, but it happened the way the officer said."

"That will be a thirty-dollar fine and court costs," snapped
the Judge. "Next case!"

"Dad," said Parson McFright's young son, "did God get
you out of it this time? Did he, Dad?"

"No, son. The only thing that I could have asked from
God was a fair trial, and that's what I got."

"Gee, that's too bad. I sure thought God would do something!"

"Maybe God did," thought Parson McFright. "Maybe God
gave me the grace to be, at least this once, an honest man."

Chapter V

Women

There were certain women in Parson McFright's parish whom he assiduously avoided, for they seemed to have an alarming effect upon his visceral system. Take Nellie Mc-Trost (and Parson McFright would). Nellie was a dazzling blonde with a curvaceous figure which she displayed to good advantage. Extremely outgoing, Nellie threw herself into one organization after another, including the church. She had an uninhibited, unselfconscious charm about her which made you think that ravishing innocence had not gone out with the Victorian age after all. To hear Nellie, Parson McFright had been a divine gift from heaven directed straight to her. She would listen to him preach, admire him with adoring, wide, blue eyes and compliment him on his sermons with a squeeze of her hand and a radiant smile. Her only regret, which she would voice with a kind of smiling petulance, was that "You never call on *me* —but then you have so many other important things to do."

"Why don't you ever drop by and see Nellie McTrost?" Parson McFright's wife asked him one day. "She's a blonde and just your type. She tells me that in all the years we've been here she's never had a parish call."

"She's around so much anyway, I thought she didn't need one," replied the parson defensively. But inwardly a battle raged between the vision of a shockingly intimate *tête-à-tête* with the voluptuous Nellie McTrost and the uncompromising clerical ideal of Nellie's right to be treated as a person rather than an object of masculine desire.

This inner conflict was probably far greater than he ever would admit, for the night that his wife reminded him of Nellie's wish Parson McFright was tormented with two nightmares, both so real that they are part of his livid experience to this very day.

NIGHTMARE NO. 1

It was night. Parson McFright was working late. His wife and children had gone to sleep after a busy day. The ring of the telephone brought him out of his reverie. With his most assuming voice he said calmly, "Parson McFright here."

"Oh, I'm so glad you're still up. This is Nellie McTrost and I'm terribly sorry to bother you at this horrible hour." Nellie's voice hummed like soft music in Parson McFright's ear.

"Not at all. What can I do for you?"

"It's Gretchen. Jim is away on a business trip, and Gretch-

en went to a friend's house just to study. She said she would
be back by ten. When she didn't return I called the Culdies,
but she hadn't even been there. I've called several of her
friends. They don't know where she is either. I'm so worried,
and I thought you might be able to help."

"I'll be right there," said Parson McFright firmly.

When he arrived, he found Nellie at the door clothed in
a housecoat, her blond hair brushed and shimmering like
that of a starlet going before the camera and the lights.

"Gretchen's here," she said in a tone of heartfelt relief. "I
got you out of bed for nothing, but I was frantic. The little
dickens has been studying all this time right next door and
lost track of time. But do come in and have a cup of coffee
or something. Frankly, I'd like some cider. How about
you?"

They sat down in the den off the main living room. Nellie
had turned on soft music and they chitchatted about many
things. The cider, which Nellie served piping hot, warmed
the parson's soul. Time seemed to flow as Nellie encouraged
him to talk glowingly about his work in a way his wife had
long since ceased to do. Occasionally and spontaneously
Nellie touched the parson's hand. Never had the parson been
so animated by feminine appeal. He wanted to dance to the
soft music, hold Nellie close. He kept struggling to find
words that would make such a step acceptable and in no
way frighten her away.

Both of them started as a car drove up the driveway. The door closed. The front latch was opened with a key.

"It's Jim," cried Nellie in surprise. "Darling, why didn't you tell me you were coming home? Come in here; you'd never guess who's here!"

Parson McFright rose to meet her husband at the door.

*   *   *   *

Sweat pouring profusely from his forehead, Parson Mc-Fright wondered sleepily whether this had been simply a nightmare or a prophetic warning from the Lord. But before he could decide the theological implications of his dream, he drifted again into the arms of Morpheus.

NIGHTMARE NO. 2

Again the phone gave forth its strident ring.

"McFright here," the parson said in his quiet, everything-is-all-right-now tone.

"O Parson McFright," said Nellie in her melodious way, "I'm so glad, so glad to find you home."

"Really? What's the matter?"

"It's not something that I want to speak about over the phone, but it is something I think I need advice on right away." There was a note of urgency in Nellie's tone. "I know it's late, but could you drop by here for a few minutes?

My husband is out of town and the children are in bed, so we can talk and be alone."

"Roger," said McFright, "I'll be there in a few minutes."

Nellie met him at the door. She was dressed like a fashion model. Her hair looked as if she had just left the beauty salon. Her housecoat, a light azure, perfectly set off the sky-blue color of her eyes. She pressed Parson McFright's hand with a wordless expression of thankfulness that he was there. She took him into the den and closed the door.

"I've got to talk to someone before my husband returns, and I knew I could depend on you."

The Parson muttered something as Nellie rushed on.

"Honestly, it all happened because my husband is away. Tonight I was invited over for dinner at the home of two of our best friends. We—that is my husband and I—were both invited, but at the last minute he called that he would have to stay over in New Orleans another day."

Nellie took out a cigarette and Parson McFright lit it, noticing a slight tremor in her hand.

"Well, to make a long story short, I went anyway. They wanted me to come. We were having a cocktail before dinner when Jane excused herself to get some last-minute items from the supermarket. You know, she had hardly stepped out when her husband tried to kiss me and hold my hand. He told me he was madly in love with me, had been for years and years, and wanted to demonstrate his love while my husband was out of town."

"This was completely unexpected?" asked Parson Mc-Fright, almost in disbelief.

"Oh, we've been friends for years. My husband has known him since long before we were married. But what shall I do? I felt so awful during dinner. I could have cried. Imagine, Jane is loyal to him. And what do I tell my husband when he returns? He'll expect we'll be seeing them as we always do." Nellie's eyes shone with the distress that made her feel so ill at ease.

"What would you do if your husband found out? How would he react?" Parson McFright's question seemed to rouse Nellie to the point of tears.

"Oh, I don't know. He's insanely jealous. He gets angry if I spend too much time with any man. I don't know what he'd do. And this is a friendship of many, many years."

"What would happen if you told Jane?"

"It would break her heart," moaned Nellie. "She loves her husband and she trusts me. If she learns the truth, we're all bound to lose."

"Do you think she'll believe you led her husband on?" Parson McFright's query seemed to startle Nellie and horrify her at the very thought.

"She knows me better than that—or at least I think so. Oh, this is horrible—it's like some terribly bad dream."

"In some respects your husband and Jane may have permitted this kind of thing to happen . . . ," Parson McFright began, but Nellie's reaction to his comment stopped him in mid-stream.

"How can you say such a thing? Really, Parson McFright, you don't know either of them at all the way I do. Why, they wouldn't hurt me any more than you . . . ."

* * * *

"My, you thrashed around last night." The parson's wife eyed her haggard spouse.

Numbly, Parson McFright agreed.

"Don't forget Nellie McTrost if you're out her way," continued his wife, kissing him goodby. "She may need some kind of help. Just because she's an attractive blonde doesn't mean that she's not human."

"Lord," muttered the parson as he drove away, "let's be honest. Who needs help from whom?"

But later in the day he made the call.

"Thanks, Lord," murmured Parson McFright.

"It's nothing," said the Lord. "It's all in a night's work."

Chapter VI

Africa

"Africa!" Parson McFright's voice fairly screamed the word into the phone. "Africa! Bishop, you can't be serious. You want me to go to Africa? What about my family? What about the church? Come to think of it, what about me?"

"Calm down, McFright." The bishop tentatively placed the receiver near his ear, which was still ringing from the last exchange. "I'm asking you because your parish would give Mahmbase an ideal picture of American church life and because you, of all people, would make the most out of your experience among the primitives there. Besides, this will only be for six months."

"Six months," McFright groaned. Six months driving a British Land-Rover in the mission area of some God-for-saken African diocese. Six months away from his wife, his children, his beloved Canaries, and all those conveniences which had come to be such a part of his life.

"But what about my church, Bishop?" McFright countered. "This Mahmbase, or whatever his name is, how will he ever be able to take my place? I'm not sure the vestry will go along with this."

"Mahmbase is a graduate of Cambridge," assured the bishop wryly. "And you know as well as I do, McFright, that your vestry will go along with anything you suggest."

"That's what I'm afraid of," thought McFright to himself.

"O.K., Bishop, I'll think it over. When do you need to know?"

"Tomorrow will do," said the bishop matter-of-factly. "You realize what a feather it will be for us to have the first African exchange, a native African, taking over one of our predominately white suburban parishes. Not to mention one of our outstanding white clergymen walking in the shoes of one of the most highly dedicated and skilled men over there. You're the man, McFright, I'm sure of it."

McFright slowly put down the receiver without bothering to say goodby. In his heart he knew he was hooked. The bishop had just touched the most vulnerable spot in his egotistic nature: his pride. McFright's pride almost always won out in spiritual battles.

The parish seemed to take the venture disgustingly well. "Gee, you're lucky to get a free trip to that hunting territory," said one man enviously. "But I don't hunt even over here," muttered McFright. The words seemed to fall on empty air.

"O Parson McFright," gushed one of the women on the women's board, "it takes courage to do something like that.

Why, I've been bragging about you to all my friends. Already they want to sign you up to show your slides of Africa at the women's club."

"Dad, can't you take me with you?" pleaded McFright's oldest son.

"I'll be lonely, of course," his wife said lovingly, "but we'll make out, and we'll keep you always in our prayers."

"I hope you'll pray good and hard," said McFright with some feeling. "I can't figure out why the bishop decided that I, of all people, was their man."

"You mean a real son of an African chief will be our priest?" said an acolyte with ill-concealed enthusiasm. "Oh, boy!"

"Great," thought McFright. "I'm being thrown to the wolves or lions or hyenas or whatever there are where I'm going."

The parish held a farewell dinner for their departing parson. Tracey, the senior warden, spoke for one and all when he concluded a number of testimonial-like speeches.

"Frankly, Padre, I never realized that the spirit of adventure, that American frontier virtue, burned so deeply in your breast. We will all miss you and look forward to your return. And now on behalf of all the folks here in the parish, let me present you this silver inscribed compass in case you are ever lost. It reads 'To our beloved Parson McFright, a shepherd who knows the path home.'"

The night before Parson McFright was to depart was a

restless one indeed. Toward midnight the telephone shattered the silence with its ominous ring.

"Parson McFright" the operator's voice sounded distant, with a somewhat foreign accent.

"Yes, I'm McFright," said McFright, quite wide awake.

"Just a minute," the operator replied.

"I say, McFright, Mahmbase here." The cultured tones seemed to put McFright's English to shame.

"Mahmbase. Oh yes, yes, how are you?"

"First rate, old chap. And I must say I'm looking forward to being with your people. Only sorry I can't meet you personally, you know. But what I called you about is that a small tribal war—kind of a feud, you know—has broken out between the people of two of my, or rather *your,* stations. Now, I've had good relationships with both chiefs. They both know you're coming, you understand. And both have agreed to respect you as if you were me, you see. It's a little sticky, but these things never last. The fact that you're coming will probably stop the whole show. Which makes it vital that you go to these stations first. There are Christians in both tribes. And we clergy are agents of reconciliation, you know. But I thought I ought to ring you up and tell you before I take off. I'll have you in my prayers. Don't worry, act with love and compassion and you'll be able to settle the whole thing. Understand? These are really lovely people, you know. Just a little primitive and all that. But

I wanted you to understand. Forewarned is forearmed, you know."

"Is there anything else?" gasped McFright.

"Splendid to talk with you, old boy," replied Mahmbase. "Hope we meet somewhere along the way. Cheerio."

"Lord," murmured McFright in anguish.

Was it his imagination, or did a voice answer, "I'm with you, old boy, you know."

Chapter VII

Depression

Parson McFright was depressed, not for one reason but for a whole raft of reasons. Nothing was going well: pledges were down; the operating fund was in the red; several fine active families had been transferred; certain other families had been conspicuously absent; he was behind on his parish calls; his sermon material seemed to lack vitality and luster; the last few meetings of the church women had been exercises in trivia; his men were far more interested in sports than the kingdom of God; and to top it off, the continual round of organized activity seemed to be pulling him farther and farther from his family.

It had been three years since he had had a nibble of a call. Now he would like to chuck his whole parish, but the powers that be seemed to have forgotten he existed. As the saying goes, he was all dressed up in his clericals with nowhere to go.

"Lord," murmured Parson McFright, "get me out of here!" There was a deafening silence to this request, and McFright was painfully aware that he was dealing as always with the hidden God.

McFright was shuffling through the mail on his desk, hoping for a God-sent call from some large and important parish desperately in need of the brilliant leadership of a man like him. There were several requests for money. There were two announcements of more meetings and the usual run of advertisements. McFright became more depressed than ever.

Beside him the omnipresent telephone jangled. "Perhaps that's my call," thought McFright wildly.

"McFright here," he answered in his most professional tone.

"O Parson McFright," a woman's voice gushed through the receiver, "you're just the one I was hoping for. The regional assembly of the Women's Protective Association is meeting at City Hall tonight. We had Dr. Waverly all set to give the invocation, but he is unable to make it. He suggested that you might be available to help out. Could you? Our committee is simply desperate."

Many confused thoughts and emotions welled up in McFright's mind including the apostolic curse upon Dr. Waverly, who had a habit of bowing out of annoying commitments at the last minute.

"Gee, it is a little late," purred McFright. "I'm afraid I am tied up," he lied. His family *did* need to see him, though not in his present state. "Why not try Pastor Fragen at the United Church? He might be able to help out."

McFright hung up the receiver, unaware that he had just

participated in the dynamics of Adam passing the buck to Eve and Eve to the snake.

McFright's meditation—if you could call it meditation—continued to spiral downward. What he needed was greener, or at least fresher, pastures. The congregation was bored with him, and he certainly was tired of them. He recalled with a shudder the advice of a certain vestryman to a fellow pastor: "The time to change parishes is when you still have one." The thought panicked him. After all, he hadn't done too bad a job, had he? Why shouldn't others be interested in *him?* He was young enough to be attractive, and old enough to be the bearer of spiritual wisdom. Everything was in his favor. So why hadn't he found favor? His was a profound mind being wasted. What a tragedy for the entire church!

How long McFright remained thus, perilously close to the outer borders of the kingdom, he never knew. What finally caught his attention and snapped him back to reality is hard to say. Call it an awareness, a consciousness of something or Someone. It is hard to put it into words. Even to put the encounter into dialogue does not do it justice. But it seems the only way to describe it in any helpful way.

"McFright!"

"Is—is that you, Lord?"

"To whose church do you belong, McFright?"

"Yours, Lord."

"Whose people do you serve?"

"Yours, Lord."

"Whose will do you obey?"

"Yours, Lord."

"Whose power do you proclaim?"

"Yours, Lord."

"Whose work do you accomplish?"

"Yours, Lord."

"Whose life do you offer?"

"Yours, Lord."

"Who called you to your task?"

"You, Lord."

"Who calls you from your task?"

"You, Lord."

"McFright."

"Yes, Lord."

"Do you have a Bible?"

"Of course, Lord."

"Matthew 6:33."

". . . Yes . . . I see what you mean, Lord. Thank you."

When true feelings, however distasteful, return to consciousness, depression disappears.

Chapter VIII

Mother's Day

Parson McFright despised Mother's Day sermons. At first he had tried to avoid them altogether, stating that Mother's Day simply was not a church holiday, but people in the parish complained or went away disappointed.

It wasn't that he was against mothers—he wouldn't have lasted long at St. Hilary's if he had been. It was just that no one listened to what the Scriptures said about marriage. Granted, people would quote bits and pieces of the Bible that justified their marital status quo, but if truth be known, the majority figured they knew far more about marriage and family life than "that old bachelor St. Paul."

The Pratletts, for example, considered that they managed a rather model Christian home. Mr. Pratlett handled all the money, gave his wife a housekeeping allowance, made all the decisions about automobiles and household appliances, and paid all the major bills. Mrs. Pratlett ordered the groceries and disciplined the children, but she referred major punishments and rulings to her husband. "After all," she remarked to a neighbor, "Mr. Pratlett *is* the head of the household."

On the surface Mrs. Pratlett was a dutiful, conscientious wife. She never complained when her husband brought business associates home for dinner unexpectedly, and she enjoyed the fact that her husband was all thumbs in the kitchen. If she desired anything out of the ordinary for herself, Mrs. Pratlett had a way of going around the problem if she thought Mr. Pratlett might disapprove. She simply asked for more housekeeping money or saved a little here and there until she could buy what she wanted.

Mr. Pratlett, on his part, sincerely tried to do his best for the family. If you could convince him that something was right, he would make every effort to do what was needed. An old Navy man, he likened their relationship to that of a ship's captain and engineer. Within the home, all decisions passed through or by him, while his wife oversaw or actually performed the major areas of household work.

The Bakers, who lived down the block, viewed the Pratlett's relationship as a bleak leftover from a bygone patriarchal era. They prided themselves in the kind of democratic system they had developed with one another and with their children. Major decisions regarding work around the home, purchases of household items, even Mr. Baker's opportunities for new employment, were made a part of the family agenda. Mrs. Baker handled all financial matters, wrote all the checks, and had a voice in any investment. On any given week Mr. Baker might help out in the kitchen or in the yard. It all depended upon what had been decided at the family "war council," as they called it.

It was generally agreed that the family came first after business hours. After all, each one theoretically had one vote, and father was no better than first among equals, and not always that. Yet Mr. Baker happily accepted his role in the true democratic spirit. "After all," he would say to his friends, "husbands and wives are equal in the sight of God. Even if the children eventually outvote us, it will be a learning experience for us all."

On Mother's Day morning both the Pratletts and the Bakers sat in the pews of St. Hilary. Mr. Pratlett had decided that the whole family should join Mother in church, for even though he insisted his children have a church background, he frequently found an excuse not to attend himself. The Baker household had voted three to two the night before to attend together.

Both families hoped that Parson McFright's sermon would be short and entertaining, yet carrying a message, a message they agreed with.

Predictably enough, Parson McFright chose as his text that portion of Paul's letter to the Ephesians which implicitly contrasts Christian marriage and the kind of marriage current in the pagan world:

Be subject to one another out of reverence for Christ. Wives, be subject to your husband, as to the Lord. For the husband is the head of the wife as Christ is the head of the church, his body, and is himself its Savior. . . . Even so husbands should

love their wives as their own bodies. For no man ever hates
his own flesh, but nourishes and cherishes it as Christ does
his church, because we are members of one body. For this reason a man shall leave his father and mother and be joined to
his wife, and the two shall become one. This is a great mystery,
and I take it to mean Christ and the church.

(Ephesians 5:21-24, 28-32)

Mrs. Baker mentally agreed that husbands and wives
should be subject to one another. After all, that is part of the
democratic spirit of interdependency. She put the rest of the
text neatly out of her mind.

Mr. Pratlett nodded his agreement that the husband is the
head of the family and then turned his mind to a projected
business contract to be settled the next day.

Mrs. Pratlett was reasonably pleased to note that she was
certainly a part of a "Christian" household, but she wondered vaguely about the husband cherishing his wife's flesh.

Both the Pratletts and the Bakers were prepared to hear
any reasonable sermon that supported their current marital
roles, but nothing that might change their opinions. None of
them absorbed Parson McFright's opening suggestion that
Paul was writing to committed Christians who had experienced a new dimension of life in Christ. So both couples sat
bolt upright when the Parson came to the major point in
his sermon.

"I have been the pastor of St. Hilary's now five years,"
said Parson McFright, "and I am convinced that we have
almost no families who enjoy a Christian marriage in the

sense of which Paul spoke. In this condemnation I include
my own.

"By this statement I do not mean to imply that we do not
have many families where husbands and wives have come
to a good working relationship. But we have few homes
where the living, risen Christ is a dynamic part of the household. Most of our families—including often my own—oper-
ate as if Easter was an event that only happened years ago,
or that Christ's risen presence can be affirmed only in the
four walls of a church.

"Paul is speaking to a live, recently converted group of
Christians in Ephesus, Christians who daily conversed with
their risen Lord, daily sought his wisdom and direction,
daily invited him to be their guest at meals, and dealt personally with him in major decisions in their lives. This daily
interaction with the present, risen Lord is the vital heartbeat
of every Christian home. Without speaking to this living
experience of yours and mine, Paul is merely verbalizing a
vague idealistic domestic blueprint instead of directing our
attention to a living, concrete aspect of our daily lives.

"Perhaps here I am pastorally in error. But while individ-
ually some of us relate directly and daily to our risen Lord,
many of us treat him as still buried in some unknown grave.
And rarely do we as families, or even as wives and husbands, speak and live our lives as though he were truly risen
from the dead."

There was more of course. Parson McFright did suggest

that Christ should be accepted as a friend in each home even as he began by accepting each one of us, that Christ's presence in our homes should be a natural companionship and would be if it were a common thing. But he had lost the vast majority of his congregation when he had pressed the idea that they might not have a Christian marriage. And the rest squirmed uneasily at the upset that might occur if Christ were really asked to be present in their home.

On that very day Mr. Pratlett decided that it would be better for the family not to attend a Mother's Day service next year if Parson McFright insisted upon being so "darn religious."

The Bakers, by secret ballot, voted 5 to 0 against attending services the following Sunday, and 5 to 0 for a Sunday fishing excursion instead.

Parson McFright's own household was somewhat unsettled by his sermon.

"Dad," asked his nine-year-old daughter with complete seriousness, "shall I set a place for Jesus?"

"It might be a helpful reminder," replied the Parson, "except he'll generally sit with us in the form of guests whom we are to treat kindly in his name."

"It's kind of spooky to think that Jesus is really here with us all the time," said his twelve-year-old son. "I'm not sure I really want to think of Jesus in that way."

"Perhaps it bothers you only because you don't know how you stand with him," replied the Parson mildly.

"Dad," questioned daughter number one, "are you sure Jesus is in this house? I thought he was in heaven on the right hand of God."

"Maybe some of your deepest moments of heaven are right here in this home," suggested her father.

"The idea I liked from Paul," Mrs. McFright called from the kitchen, "was the fact that Christ came from God to become one with the human race, which is like the way a man leaves his father and mother and becomes one with his wife. There's something awesome and mysterious and real about that. Why didn't you say anything about it?"

"I didn't catch it," said Parson McFright ruefully. But then he brightened. "By gosh," he said, "the way we're talking maybe the Lord has gotten his foot into our home after all."

Chapter IX

Calling

Parson McFright hesitated a moment as he looked at the fashionable home where he was to make his call. The woman had not darkened the door of St. Hilary's for three months. He'd seen her husband only off and on. Their high school children had dropped away like shooting stars.

He was greeted warmly, but with raised and inquiring eyebrows.

"You've kind of vanished from my line of vision," he offered as a place to begin.

"It's been three months," the woman said firmly, "and it may be three years—perhaps never again. As far as I'm concerned it's been a real relief to get St. Hilary's out of my life."

"I didn't realize the church was such a source of trouble for you." McFright reacted, somewhat perplexed.

"Oh, you know I've questioned things all along: your confirmation program, the getting up on Sunday morning, the whole rat-race of getting children ready for church school. Don't get me wrong. I'm just talking about *our* particular household. It just doesn't work out. And ever since I've severed all connections with it, I've felt great. Really."

"You finally have taken a stand for what you believe in," McFright stalled for equilibrium.

"That's just it. It's the thing to go to church. It's our duty, we told ourselves. But we reached a point when we weren't getting a thing out of the church services. At first we did. At times your sermons have been very helpful. But we've just seemed to have grown right past where the church is meaningful at all."

There's no parson who likes to see a family slip out of his reach, especially one that he likes and admires. Parson McFright was well aware that maintaining a family in St. Hilary's satisfied not only his egotistic needs but was one way in which he evaluated his own efforts and his vestry evaluated him.

He could feel himself getting defensive. In past encounters over church-going he had tried to manipulate people into feeling guilty about what they were doing to themselves or to the church. He sensed cloven horns prodding him to chastise this smiling woman within an inch of her sinful life. But this knowledge didn't make the parson any less devil-resistant. He was in a position similar to that of the advertising executive who realizes a prized account is slipping unexpectedly away. In these moments, when an inner battle waged, the parson's outward countenance seemed peculiarly benign.

"I'm still not quite sure I understand you," he said, playing for time.

"I didn't expect you would," the woman replied, "I'm not even sure I understand this myself. All I can say is that I don't feel guilty about it. I've never felt better. The church has been helpful in the past; it just no longer is, that's all. I have resented its dogmatic old-fashioned attitudes toward divorce, its worn-out hymns with the old-fashioned words. But they didn't bother me to a point. Now I'm growing up, or at least I think I am. I don't want to do something just out of duty when my heart and mind say that the church stands for something which is antiquated, if not altogether wrong."

The inner artillery exchange in Parson McFright's soul subsided unexpectedly.

"You know, I'd like to make you feel very wrong and guilty about what you're saying," he blurted out. "In part you may be right, but when you split off from the church, you fragment it some more. Listening to you makes me feel like a football coach watching some of his best players walk off the field."

"Flattery may help, but it will get you nowhere." The woman smiled implacably.

"What I mean," said McFright plunging on, "is that there is something about what you're saying that sounds as though I should try my darndest to support you, but you're also suggesting that I'm a pastor of a kind of half-way station, that the church is useful for a time until one rises beyond it. I guess no one likes to think another has gone beyond him spiritually any more than he likes to see someone go past him professionally."

"Now you're being difficult." The woman reacted strongly for the first time. "I'm not saying we're any better than others in the church at all! I'm not even saying that I, or the rest of the family—I can't speak for them—may not become active and happy in the church at some time in the future. All I'm saying is it's a relief to stop doing something out of duty, something that has disturbed more than helped me. And this doesn't mean God doesn't figure in our lives. In some ways I've been closer to God since I took this stand than before."

"I suppose Christ thought of the church of his day in the same way," mused Parson McFright, "and yet Luke tells us that he was in the synagogue on the sabbath day as was his custom."

"Well, that was a long time ago," replied the woman. "Besides, he was different from us. How do you know he would have gone to the synagogue if he lived in the twentieth century? Anyhow, I've heard an awful lot of jokes to the effect that he can't even get into churches today. Maybe I'm closer to him outside than in."

"I hope you realize I'm not talking about the building when I speak of the church," said Parson McFright, getting up to go. "The church is people like you and me worshiping and living with Christ. I know it sounds funny, but your

being with me on Sunday supports my faith even as I hope
my presence encourages you."

"It doesn't justify my feeling miserable." The woman
tenaciously stood her ground. "You can't say we haven't
tried. And as I said, this may not last—we may try again.
When I don't know."

"O.K.," said the Parson at the door, "I trust we're friends.
I just had to use the shepherd's crook. Hope you'll consider
why Jesus stayed with the church in his day even though it
crucified him."

"That's all right," the woman said, getting the last word,
"in the first place I'm not Jesus. And the way I've been feeling I'm not the one who's been lost but the one who has
been found."

*   *   *   *

That night Parson McFright recalled the encounter before
going to sleep. "I wonder if she was right," he thought to
himself. "Maybe the Lord found her after all."

Not many miles away the woman pounded her pillow in
anger. "What right does that Parson McFright have butting
into my spiritual life? The more I think about it the angrier
I get."

"He's just watching over his flock," said her husband
soothingly.

"That's what I'm afraid of," the woman replied.

Chapter X

Results

"The reason the church doesn't really get very far with me, McFright, is that it isn't clear about the results it hopes to accomplish through me."

The businessman who addressed these words of wisdom to Parson McFright twisted the cigar in his mouth and looked balefully at the clergyman seated across from him.

McFright seemed puzzled.

"You don't get me, do you?" said the man, shifting his cigar. "Well, let me put it differently. A few years ago my wife finally won out, and I went through that confirmation class of yours. Frankly I enjoyed it. But you never told us where we went from there after we were confirmed. I feel like a man who went through some form of officer candidate school, and then was commissioned but never assigned duty—kind of sitting around awaiting orders."

"I've seen you ushering lately," Parson McFright began lamely.

"Yes, and I upped my pledge and served on that contemptible vestry of yours, too, you'll remember. And that brings me to another point." The cigar was now violently moving up and down, causing a kind of hypnotic glaze in the Parson's eyes.

"That vestry. They argue over every nickel and dime, spend hours quibbling over nothing. If they were running their own operation they would really get things done." The businessman was rapidly taking the role of a learned inquisitor, and McFright shifted uneasily in his seat.

"I suppose they feel that the money from the offering is not theirs," said McFright defensively. "It's a trust which people want them to spend wisely."

"Oh heck! I mean really, Padre, I've sat on that vestry for three miserable years. Every one's a Simon Legree about buying a coffee machine or office postage, yet they'll spend thousands of dollars for a new building at the drop of a hat. A new building gives them a sense of direction. They can see the results. Hang the cost if they can see something concrete. But you know what happens most of the time. They watch the balance sheet like a sick man watching a nurse read his temperature. And all because they don't really know what they're supposed to be accomplishing other than maintaining buildings and paying the parson a living wage. These are the only goals they feel called to meet."

"But it isn't that simple," expostulated McFright. "How do I know what God wishes to accomplish through you? That's between you and God. The results are up to God too. 'Except the Lord build the house they labor but in vain to build it.' If the undertaking be of men it will fail; but if it is of God, you will not be able to overthrow it."

Having quoted and paraphrased Scripture McFright rested more comfortably in his chair. The businessman, however, was noticeably unimpressed.

"Well, if you want to put it that way, the results of my vending machine business are up to God, too. But that doesn't mean I don't have a vision of my goals. Our object is to manufacture a vending machine which will put the customer's product in front of the public in such a way that he not only sees it but can put his grubby little mitts right on it. We have to produce machines that will serve our customers' needs and get their products sold. And we have to do so in such a way that we make a profit. My job is to see we make a profit. My salesmen get the customers. My designers make the machines to specifications, and my market people tell me what machines make the product most attractive in a given area, and where the product can be sold most effectively. Our research men are constantly testing out new machines. Our plant manager is required to watch quality and operating costs. But the goal of everyone involved, all the way down the line, is to sell vending machines for a profit. And as long as we are sensitive to our God-given opportunities, we do all right. So I don't see why you can't say our business is as much in the hand of God as the church is. All I want to know from you is what that church expects of *me*. Put something in there in place of 'vending machines' and something in there for 'profit' and I'll get off your back. This thing has been bothering me for a long time."

With that the man snuffed out the last shredded remains of his cigar and sat back expansively, challenging Parson McFright to come through.

Parson McFright didn't answer immediately. It was true, he conceded, that some Christian churches apparently have a more definite answer to the question of results. For some, the goal was to have everyone make a clear-cut, public decision for Christ; some churches wanted every person to experience the power of the Holy Spirit, to speak in tongues, and to exercise the gifts of the Spirit; still others wanted everyone baptized and confirmed in the One True Church. There was nothing inherently wrong with any of these aims, mused McFright, but were they really final ends or only means to a greater end?

Out loud he said, "I suppose we are called as Christians to help others love God, themselves, and their neighbors in such a way that everlasting life with God is not only believable but desirable. Or to put it in New Testament terms, to help others live and become aware of what Jesus called the kingdom of God. But I don't know if that's concrete enough for you. And as far as profit is concerned, when you are touched now by the kingdom of God you spontaneously want to offer your substance in gratitude to God, and to help others hear and believe the good news."

"That all may mean something to you, but it sounds pretty

churchy to me," muttered the businessman as though his mind was seeking something far away. "Can you put it in two words—two simple words? What's your purpose? What results do you wish to accomplish? Simple—for a guy like me."

"Well, you may not buy this either," said the Parson thoughtfully, "but if you as a Christian, wherever you go, were to present Christ in some way or another so that others could have abundant life, it seems to me that would say the same thing."

"I am to *present Christ* in order that others may have *abundant life*." The businessman thought this over for a long time. "I can buy this 'abundant life' bit, but I'm not at all sure I feel comfortable about 'presenting Christ' to anyone. Do you mean verbally, witnessing, helping others, preaching?"

"I'm not sure exactly what I mean," said McFright. "I'm not sure whether I'm talking about introducing someone to Christ or merely offering yourself to him because you are Christ's man. But somehow as Christians we should be able to represent Christ in such a way that others may love life, honestly face reality, and savor something significant of God, man, and the universe because we are with them."

It was the businessman now who appeared thoughtful. "I hear you," he said, gazing off into the sky. "I hear your words. Are you suggesting that I don't have to make an effort to make everyone a Christian?"

"Is everyone a customer for your vending machine?" queried McFright, not quite sure whether the analogy would hold up.

"There are a lot more customers than my salesmen dig up," replied the businessman with feeling, "and I never let them forget it. But I grant you everyone doesn't need or want my vending machines, even though everyone probably at some time or another should want the products our machines provide."

"O.K.," said McFright, "so also does everyone need Christ and his kingdom, but perhaps not packaged the way Christians are capable of offering it. Something in the back of McFright's conscience cringed a bit at the direction the conversation was taking. He was not sure whether his bishop or the doctors of the church would approve his theology.

"On the other hand," continued McFright, "look at the way God draws our attention to the reality of the kingdom through Christ and through Christian people. Is there any better demonstration of God's love and power than in Jesus' life, death, and resurrection—or for that matter in the self-sacrificing efforts of Christ's church in the power of his Holy Spirit?"

"Tell me," pursued McFright, "what did your confirmation mean to you when you accepted Jesus Christ as your Lord and Savior? Didn't this somehow affect your relationship with God so that under certain circumstances you could share your experience?"

There was a long pause.

Parson McFright looked quizzically at the businessman across the table. The latter smiled. "I was thinking about the competitors," the man said, "you know—the Buddhist, the Muslim, the Communist, or the humanist, if you like. . . ."

"And?" asked McFright.

"Well." The businessman laughed. "I guess the church is no different than my operation after all. When my men are worried about the competition I say: 'Men, we can never prove that we have the finest vending machines on the market, although we can show in various ways how our machines can do as well or outdo others. But if you are genuinely concerned and interested in your customers' realistic needs, then we have a company which in its field can meet those needs. And if we do, we will be around a long, long time.' So I guess in the last analysis we should neither ignore our competition nor worry too much about him. We can only be true to our convictions, be open to opportunities, and leave the final results in the hands of God."

Back home that evening, Parson McFright shared some of the conversation with his wife.

"I suppose I have no right to disagree with you, dear," his wife said, "but frankly I prefer 'receive Christ' rather than 'present Christ.' After all, I'm a novice at things like this."

"You're just being feminine, that's all," grumbled McFright, "but between you and me maybe 'presenting' and 'receiving' are just two halves of the same coin. Maybe we are to present Christ to God and man to receive Christ from God and man, in order that we may have life and have it more abundantly."

"I guess that means we have to keep alert to the many ways God does send Christ into our lives and be very open to the ways we may offer him to others along the way," said his wife thoughtfully.

Chapter XI

Discipleship

The man burst into Parson McFright's study with hardly a knock at the door.

"I did it!" he exclaimed triumphantly. "I did just what you suggested Sunday. I told my boss that he could go you know where. I really told him off, and I wanted you to be the first to know."

Parson McFright opened his mouth as much in astonishment as to speak, but the man rushed on.

"There is one little favor I'd like to ask. Would you come home with me when I break the news to the little woman? She's been pretty proud of my job and I'm afraid she may get a little upset when I tell her. And there's a little matter about another parishioner of yours."

"Have a seat." McFright had recovered slightly. "Back up a bit, will you? Tell me what happened."

"I did just what I should have done two years ago! I walked into the old man's office—the old Scrooge was looking over all those financial reports showing him all the money he'd made—and I told him he could get a new man to do his lousy, dirty work."

"And . . . ?"

"He got red in the face, blew up like a balloon. Told me to shag my tail out of there—that no one, but no one, could talk to him like that and that I had one hour to get all my things out of the office. And then he was so upset he went storming out of there. . . ."

"So . . . ?"

"So, I emptied by desk, and then I went back to his office for a last word. He hadn't come back. I pulled out the rug from under his chair and threw it on the desk and told his secretary to give him my compliments."

"So now you're out of a job . . . . I'm sorry," said McFright.

"No, don't be sorry. I should have done this ages ago. I wouldn't have had the courage except for what you said Sunday in your talk."

"In my talk Sunday . . . . you . . . you mean about Christ driving the money-changers out of the temple? I don't get the connection exactly."

"Remember, you said there are moments when Christians should get angry. That there is a difference between righteous indignation—when someone is being hurt or man is disgracing something holy—and the selfish kind of anger when we take out our guilt and frustrations on someone else. Well, up to then I had thought all anger—and I've had a pretty hot temper—was kind of unchristian, so to speak. But the minute you said it something inside me stung me like a bee. I realized that I'd been angry for years over the way my boss had made me treat our customers, and that the only reason I'd taken it was because I was too cotton-picking scared to tell him off."

"You were afraid you'd lose your job?"

"You're darn right! I've got four mouths to feed, you know, not counting my own."

"But wouldn't your boss listen to you? Did you have to blow sky high the way you did?" McFright was somewhat aghast at what he had triggered in the man.

"The Scripture I heard didn't say Christ tried to talk nicely to all those money-changers and sellers in the temple. No, I've tried to talk with him several times and all he said was to leave policy to him and tend to my own knitting. I had to put it the way I did or he'd never have believed there was anything wrong about the way he does his business. If I'd quit like a gentleman, it wouldn't have done anything to his ulcer." The man smiled slyly.

"But what does he have you doing that's so wrong? Can you share this with me without breaking any confidences? Is your business illegal—are you smuggling dope on the side?"

"Oh no, nothing like that." The man sounded a little less euphoric and settled back in his chair. It's just that some of my customers have become my good friends over the years, and the majority of them really trust me. I mean that. And our product is competitive, you know, so you need to work the angles to get the business. The boss's motto is 'If our product does not have an unfair advantage over the competition we have to maintain an unfair advantage with the buyer.' "

"You're not implying blackmail . . . . " McFright sounded horrified.

"No, no, nothing as crude as that."

"Bribery, then—favors of some kind?"

"No, much more subtle than that. Our boss says that any salesman caught bribing a customer, no matter what the order, will be fired on the spot. It's bound to backfire. No, we are to develop the image of trust—par excellence. We're not to give our customers presents or take them out to dinner unless absolutely necessary. We're to help them, ask nothing of them but a fair share of their business. We're to play it above board all the way. We are the square shooter in the trade. It's part of the policy."

"Sounds pretty good to me," McFright averred.

"Clever is the word," continued the man. "The catch comes at the moment of the sale. It's a matter of the price. Every salesman knows the bottom limit that the product can be sold for—and the top. It's worked out in advance. We look the customer straight in the face and give him the highest figure we think he can stand. We look him square in the eye and tell him that that's the fairest price for our company as well as for his. Half the time, with the trust we've built up over the years, he believes us and we have a sale, based not on bribery or blackmail, mind you, but on trust."

"And what if he thinks you are too high?"

"Oh, we dial a certain number, make a phony call to the office and come in with a special price just because he is a good customer and we want to do him a favor. If he still won't budge we return to our position of honesty and come back another time. But it's all a fake. We build up something sacred, like a relationship of trust, and then desecrate it knowingly. It's part of policy—it's good business."

At that moment the walls of the office were shattered by what sounded like the roar of an angry lion. Through the walls came a loud voice.

"But I must see Parson McFright immediately . . . . it's urgent!"

"Holy smoke, that sounds like my boss!" The man started in his chair.

"It sounds to me like the treasurer of the church," said McFright. "Don't tell me . . . . "

"Didn't you know?" said the man in a surprised voice, "he brought us to St. Hilary's. I said there was a small matter to be straightened out between two parishioners."

"Lord," cried Parson McFright inwardly, "I'll be out of a job."

"Nonsense, McFright," a voice seemed to answer. "Here's where the job begins."

Chapter XII

Edna Grainridge

Edna Grainridge was the poorest, yet in many ways the richest, person in Parson McFright's parish. A widow for some fifteen years, she lived alone in a small two-bedroom home in one of the older sections of Tri-City. It was hard to guess her age, but the estimates started in at around seventy-five. Yet there was something so remarkably spry about her that it made you wonder.

For one thing Edna walked a mile and a half to church. By actual count ninety-five percent of St. Hilary's parish came by car even if they lived three blocks away. Even in the most severe winter blasts Edna would arrive pink-cheeked and cheerful while the rest of the parishioners groused about the beastly weather they had experienced between the parking lot and the church door.

Then, too, it was almost impossible to wait on Edna. She said it was because she was so used to waiting on herself. If there was coffee to be served, Edna was generally pouring it; if the kitchen needed to be picked up, Edna would stay around after the others left to lend a helping hand or to do the whole job herself.

"Oh, come on, Edna, sit down," people would say. But she would only smile in her friendly way. And usually folks were too comfortable having her wait on them to make any effort to change her mind.

Financially Edna was poor. She lived on social security and a very small annuity which her husband had hoped would be adequate. Yet she managed to offer five dollars a week for the spread of Christ's kingdom—a fact which caused one steward of St. Hilary to double his pledge in shame. But Edna thought nothing of it, only regretting she had no more to give. "It's very little," she would say of any effort on her part for the church. "I am so grateful for everything God has given me." And Edna sincerely was. She appreciated life. She enjoyed people and was willing to serve in any humble way. For this reason Edna was rich in the blessings of the kingdom which, as Christ showed well, begins in the here and now of this present world.

With this as background you can imagine the shock that went through Parson McFright's very being when the police called him to headquarters. A woman in custody by the name of Edna Grainridge had requested that he visit her.

"Edna Grainridge! You're not serious! It just can't be!" Parson McFright expostulated over the phone.

"It can't be, but it is," was the wry reply.

Edna appeared outwardly calm and just a trifle embarrassed when Parson McFright was ushered into her cell.

"I'm terribly sorry to have troubled you, Parson Mc-

Fright," she began. "I know how busy you are. And I hope I will not take too much of your time. But I live alone you know, and I'm worried about my cat. I wonder if you will take my house key, get my cat, and take it to the neighbors on the corner. They have a little girl who just loves to play with it, and my cat shouldn't be any trouble for them at all."

"Do you mind, Edna, if I sit down?" asked Parson Mc-Fright.

"Oh, forgive me, Parson, you do look a little pale. Are you all right?"

"Edna," began McFright, "I'll take care of the cat, but will you please tell me just why you are here—in jail?"

"They tell me the charge is shoplifting," Edna stated matter-of-factly.

"You mean—you stole? That's hard to believe, Edna."

"They discovered stolen property on my person," Edna corrected.

"What did you steal?" asked McFright with a look of plain incredulity still upon his face.

"I had two wrist watches, a pocket compass and a large box of bubblegum in my possession."

"Bubblegum!" exploded McFright. "Oh, I get it, you're covering for someone else. But Edna, they don't put a person like you in jail for stealing bubblegum even if you did steal it, and I don't think you did."

"They do when there's been a long series of petty thefts

going on. The chief of detectives is very angry," said Edna. "He—the detective—was very annoyed with me. He told me that I could ask for a lawyer and that he would put me in a quiet place to think things over."

"Look, Edna," Parson McFright said after a pause, "you must be protecting someone else."

She stood up. "Please don't ask me any more questions, Parson McFright. I believe I know what I am doing. I was caught in the act and will take my punishment. If you will take my cat to the neighbor I will be very grateful."

It was obvious that Edna wished Parson McFright to leave. A little dazed, the Parson meekly motioned for the guard to let him out. "I'll keep in touch with you, Edna. Don't you want a lawyer or something?"

"Nothing, thank you." Edna was perfectly firm.

The chief of detectives stopped Parson McFright as he was leaving.

"What do you think of our thief?" he asked.

"It's impossible," said McFright. She's obviously covering up for someone she knows—some young delinquent or other."

"That's what we thought," the detective growled. "But the store manager swears that she was in the store alone. There was no child, no kids anywhere near her when she was caught."

"But bubblegum, wrist watches, and a compass! It just doesn't add up. Besides, she very carefully told me she was caught with these items in her possession. She never admitted stealing anything."

"Well, I've run into some queer things before," said the detective. "I kind of hoped that someone like you could talk some sense into her head. I won't keep her overnight, but I'll have to charge her with petty theft. And by gosh, she just may be the one who has been in on some of the shoplifting in this area."

"Have you checked her home?" asked McFright.

"Right away. Found nothing. Nothing." The detective was clearly frustrated.

That night Parson McFright tossed and turned. It couldn't be, it just couldn't be. Yet, he of all people believed that sin was a part of the make-up of every human being, even of an Edna Grainridge. But the person just didn't match the crime, unless she was trying to protect another party in some way. But who? And why?

Toward morning Parson McFright fell into a deep sleep. He awoke with a start, crying out in a loud voice that shook up the entire household, "I've got it, I've got it!"

"Got what?" asked his wife, sleepily. "What's wrong, Dad?" called his children.

"Nothing. Everything's all right. I just got the idea I've been looking for."

The Parson dressed quickly. He dashed out of the house without even considering breakfast and drove hastily to the home of Edna Grainridge, who had been released in time to retrieve her cat from the neighbors.

"Why, Parson McFright!" Edna exclaimed. "It's good to see you, but isn't this rather early for a parish call?"

"Edna," said McFright sternly, "just answer me one question. Do you chew bubblegum?"

"If you put it that way—no," said Edna Grainridge. But she added hastily, "There are lots of young people who get a great deal of enjoyment from it. Maybe I should start."

"O.K., Edna," Parson McFright said grimly, "let me tell you what I think, though you don't have to agree with me at all. Suppose you knew someone—a boy or girl who has been in a shoplifting gang—someone you cared a great deal about. And suppose you talked to him about it but it didn't change his attitude one bit. Suppose he couldn't see why you should be concerned or embarrassed that a friend of yours was doing this kind of thing. And just suppose, now, that you couldn't tell the police about what you knew without losing this friendship altogether. So you decide to shoplift yourself and get caught, to get convicted and get all the publicity. Maybe this person or persons might suddenly wake up to what they were doing—or might potentially be doing to those who loved them—and change. Maybe they wouldn't change; but some rather stubborn, kind of far-out person might take the chance. What do you think?"

"That's an interesting theory, Parson McFright," said

Edna Grainridge with a slight smile around her lips. And they left it just that way.

In the ensuing days Edna Grainridge was charged with shoplifting and pleaded guilty as charged. The judge sentenced her to court costs and gave her a severe lecture but otherwise was satisfied, since the stolen items had been returned.

When the news of her conviction was published in the local newspaper, St. Hilary's parish reacted, as had Parson McFright, in stunned surprise. Instead of the usual gossip, though, people seemed to agree to forget the whole thing publicly; but on the side they would drop by to say hello or write Edna a small card of encouragement. At church no one would bring the matter up, for if they tried they were sure to receive a nasty look. "We just don't talk about it."

About a month later Edna Grainridge appeared somewhat apologetically at Parson McFright's office.

"I'm sorry to trouble you, Parson McFright," she said, "but could I have a moment of your time?"

"Absolutely, Edna, come in and have a chair."

"Well, really I don't know how to begin. I know I've caused you and so many people in the parish a great deal of embarrassment by my carryings-on. But I just wanted to tell you that you were not far wrong in that theory that you shared with me. I'm only a little disappointed that I can't be sure everything will work out."

"Did the person or persons ever speak with you?" asked the parson.

"Yesterday for the first time," said Edna. "That's why I'm here."

"What did he or she say?"

"*He* said I was stupid."

"Stupid because you were caught?"

"No, just stupid. That's what I wanted to ask you. I kind of thought that was a good sign."

"Could be . . ." said Parson McFright.

Chapter XIII

A Call

"We're looking for a man—not too young, not too old—one who will appeal to our youth." The chairman of the calling committee evidently spoke the mind of the group, for all heads nodded in agreement.

"Of course we want someone who can preach a good sermon," added a second member of the committee. Again heads nodded.

It was obvious to Parson McFright that by implication he was being complimented both as a man who might work well with their young people and as a preacher who would come through. It was tempting to let these remarks go by as though there was a mutual understanding. However, he took another tack.

"What would you say if I told you that the most effective pastor is one who helps adults deal with their own youth, and that a good sermon does not always communicate the true, biblical Gospel. In my present parish I'm afraid the people want me to do what they are unable to do: to be free and effective with the very young people they can't reach. I'll admit I'd like to be popular with our young people and with their parents, but I must say that often I don't feel mature enough or clever enough or loose enough to do it."

"Oh, well, we'll take our chances." The chairman of the calling committee obviously wanted to by-pass sticky questions. His object clearly was to find the right man; after that, things would surely take care of themselves. But Parson McFright was not a man to be brushed aside lightly.

"No, seriously," he pressed his point, "are you gentlemen willing to work personally with me with your youth, or are you after a person who will take the responsibility off your shoulders?"

"I think you can rest assured that you would have our entire support." The senior warden of St. Swithens spoke with conviction. "And frankly, Parson, it will be a pleasure to hear the Bible preached rather than politics." The committee again nodded in unanimous agreement.

"You're going to think I'm just being difficult"—the parson twisted in his chair—"but it seems to me that the entire Bible witnesses to the political storms that accompanied the ministry of the prophets—not to mention David or Moses. Wasn't our Lord killed as a political scapegoat?"

It was clear that the natives—the native churchmen, that is—were getting restless. Several of them were privately having some second thoughts about the man who was confronting them. Others were thinking of pressing personal matters that needed attention, either at home or at the office.

"I'm sure this is just a matter of words." The chairman entered into the conversation as if to terminate it. "Frankly, Parson McFright, I'm sure that your viewpoint and ours are not far apart at all. If you stick to the Bible—to where you are the expert—you won't have any trouble, none whatsoever."

To a man, heads nodded. Several members of the committee stood up as if to leave. There didn't seem a courteous way to bring the group back to the questions. The parson let the matter drop.

That same day the chairman of the calling committee chatted briefly with the senior warden over the phone. "Maybe he isn't our man after all. I'm not sure we see eye to eye about this political stuff. If the preachers would stick to things they know, like the Bible, and lay off the other things they don't know, the whole church would be better off."

"You forget we checked him out rather thoroughly." The chairman was reassuring. "There haven't been any problems in his current parish. Frankly, I admired his courage in bringing the issues up."

"I suppose so," replied the warden. "I just wondered how you felt."

"How did it go?" Parson McFright's wife was obviously concerned.

"I'm not sure," he replied. "We didn't really come to grips

with what they expected me to do with their youth, or what was meant by 'biblical sermons' or by 'politics.' I have a feeling that we were afraid to level with each other."

"What are you going to do?" asked his wife, wondering if she should start to pack or continue to relax in her present surroundings.

"I've decided to write a letter," replied her husband, and he did.

Gentlemen:

I appreciate, sincerely appreciate, being asked to become pastor of St. Swithens. Your parish seems all one might desire, and I'm personally flattered that you would call me.

However, before we start under false premises, I for one would appreciate two more hours of your time to go over again some of the questions we were discussing before our meeting broke up. I'm not sure if you see me as *the* minister, or as a minister among ministers—that is to say, a kind of playing coach. If the parish is to be Parson McFright's church, we are starting off on the wrong foot.

Nor am I clear if I know what "biblical preaching" means to you, or what "political sermons" mean to either of us. It seems to me that Christianity is related to every aspect of our lives. I certainly wish to be free to speak biblically about political matters in the same way that I might speak biblically about sexuality, family tensions, or church affairs. I hope it will be possible for you to speak to me in the same vein.

Can this meeting be arranged? If so, may it be on the basis that if you still wish to have me you will issue a second call? But by the same line of reasoning, you are under no obligation to re-issue your call to me.

Sincerely,
Parson McFright

"What do you think of the letter?" His wife was far wiser in certain matters than her spouse.

"I think I'll start painting the kitchen," she remarked wryly. "We may be at St. Hilary's a long, long time."

"Don't you think I'm being honest?" said the Parson, a trifle put out.

"Oh, you're being honest, all right. But there's a certain kind of honesty that is effective after you've established a relationship, and then there's the kind that drops the iron curtain. Perhaps that letter will be too much for the calling committee to take. You're pushing them rather far, farther than they may wish to go."

"You women never get directly to the point," grumbled the parson. "Sometimes it's days before you'll come right out and say what's on your mind. I think the men on this committee are different."

"Okay," sighed his wife resignedly, "be direct. But if they feel about you as I sometimes do, it may be the last you'll hear from them for quite some time."

"If God had become woman, we would never have heard the Word," growled the parson darkly.

"I wonder if God ever did make one teeny-weeny mistake," she answered lightly. "Would a woman have been crucified in a man's world? . . . But then again," she mused, "maybe God did send the one man who heeded feminine wisdom every now and then."

Chapter XIV

The Hunter

There exist certain women—inside the church as well as outside—who can set up social situations fairly charged with potential drama. One such woman was Lillian Van der Water, who among other things was an active member of St. Hilary's. One example of Lillian's peculiar talent was that housewarming she conceived once over morning coffee, a minor triumph since the unsuspecting husband was in his new bathtub when his friends arrived. Or again, there was that contrived meeting set up by Lillian between a well-to-do widower and an attractive female friend of Lillian's, a woman who, according to Lillian, "should have been married years ago." The couple eloped two weeks later without phoning her.

So it was that Lillian, in her usual form, invited Parson McFright and his wife to meet "some perfectly delightful friends of ours"—the "delightful" husband being an outspoken atheist. Of course Lillian and the "delightful" wife had planned the maneuver for weeks. The problem was not with the McFrights but with the outspoken husband who "would be darned" if he'd eat a meal with some "mealy-mouthed clergyman." And besides, as Harry Cochrane, the "delightful" husband, once put it, "Don't get me involved with any preacher. I'll just get into some blasted argument."

You can imagine with what anticipation Lillian Van der Water brought Parson McFright and Harry Cochrane face to face. On the surface it had to look as though Harriet Cochrane was the mere victim of circumstance. After all, how could she dictate whom the Van der Waters might have as guests in their home? Harry, being an avid sportsman, had flown up to Canada for a week and could not expect consultation over social plans made in his absence. The matter-of-fact statement, "We're going over to the Van der Water's for dinner" was accepted without a murmur. For the moment he felt just a little guilty for having been away from Harriet so long.

So Harry Cochrane suspected nothing—nor for that matter did Parson McFright—until after the introductions, when Harry led with the usual question, "Say, what do you do for a living, McFright?"

McFright gave his usual carefree answer, "Oh, I don't work for a living, I'm the pastor at St. Hilary's." He was somewhat taken aback by the look of horror that spread over Harry's face, an expression which, for days thereafter, Lillian gleefully described to her friends. Harriet Cochrane artfully managed to avoid her husband's glaring eyes.

"You'll have to look out for Harry, Parson McFright,"

interposed Lillian. "He says he's an atheist, but that's only an excuse for hunting, fishing, and golfing fifty-two weekends a year."

And so the bell sounded for round one. But it was several moons before either Parson McFright or Harry Cochrane realized that they had been maneuvered into what Lillian exaggeratedly would call "the battle of the year."

Harry Cochrane proceeded to do what he usually did when his wife put him in an awkward situation: he set out to embarrass her with his blunt mannerisms. Only this time it was just what his wife wanted him to do.

"Heck, McFright, you might as well know the truth. I am an atheist. But I like to hunt and get out of doors. I reverence nature, if you want to call that atheism. Matter of fact, I just flew back from a little fishing in Canada."

At this point the fight might have slowed down to a social draw, for Parson McFright was a wild-eyed fisherman himself. But neither Harriet nor Lillian was of a frame of mind to let this opportunity for confrontation slip by. Like the picadors who prod the bull they struck.

"I don't see why Harry can't accept that God created nature, can you, Parson McFright?" asked Lillian. "After all, how did nature or anything come into being if it weren't for God or some power behind it?"

"The way I understand it," said Harriet, "if nature is god, then might makes right, survival is for the fittest, and women are just here to be bred by any strong male who happens along. What chance have we got if all men have a god like Harry's?"

"Listen, Harriet," interrupted Harry, "in nature the females do just as well as the males if not better—just like you. But what I like about nature is that its creatures are open and honest. They do instinctively what they have to do. They fight, they breed, they enjoy themselves, and they don't feel guilty about it. When they live they live, and when they die they die. No bear gets up before a group of other bears and lectures about a bear heaven or a bear hell. The way I see things is that sincere people like you, Parson McFright, have made us humans into guilty, dishonest hypocrites. You set up laws and tell people they won't get to heaven unless they obey them, so that if people are to live at all, they have to hide what they've done; or if they don't want to live, they obey the rules and hope that there'll be some sort of accounting in the great by and by. Me, I want to make the best of this one life and live now."

"That's why Harry has collected so many traffic tickets along with his elk heads," slipped in Harriet. "He doesn't believe in obeying laws."

"Honey, you know that just isn't true." Harry sounded misunderstood. "I believe society needs rules. For the self-preservation of man it needs rules. But the way I see it, the church has tried to scare people into obeying laws by promising them an eventual life in some kind of happy hunting ground, which just isn't true. I'm doing my hunting while

I'm alive because I don't expect to get another chance after I'm dead."

"Why don't you give Parson McFright a chance to speak, dear?" his wife interjected. "I asked him a question a minute ago and you've never given him a chance to say one word."

"I like to hunt, too," began McFright, "just as I enjoy getting out of doors. It's just as Harry said. He's an atheist and doesn't believe in a God who cares anything for him. I'm a Christian and believe God created us, loves us, accepts us, forgives us, and desires a personal relationship with us. To me human love is different from animal love, although it includes certain aspects of it, just as God's love is different from human love and yet includes certain human elements in it."

"O.K.," said Harry, "but don't you honestly teach people that unless they obey the commandments or try to be good they won't get to heaven?"

"You first have to believe in heaven," replied McFright, "and in my terms that means experiencing and accepting God's love for you now. Laws or commandments or rules of society are just one way in which God expresses his love —by my human love toward my neighbor."

"Parson McFright has trouble with traffic laws too." The parson's wife spoke for the first time.

"I didn't say a Christian always obeyed the laws, did I?" The parson's wife could put him on the defensive faster than anybody. "All I'm saying is that laws are *one* way in which man expresses God's love humanly to his fellow man. If a law is arbitrary or wrong, a Christian out of love may have to break it. Though I must say I break them usually because I'm just plain selfish and inconsiderate. But I'm getting away from my main point. Why would I want to be with you or God in heaven, or be myself everlastingly in heaven, unless I had found something in you or God or myself that was worth continuing? First I have to find a relationship with one who has the power to transform me into a more loving person. This involves putting me in a community of persons with whom I can be honest, who will accept and forgive me and support me in my struggle to love. This is why the church as well as Christ is so important to me. I'm not so naive that I believe heaven is for me alone. But I agree with you, Harry, that I want to live now. It's the now of God's love, communicated to me through Christ, through people and events, that gives me the hope of any life to come."

"But doesn't the Bible say that those who 'raise Cain' and 'live it up' won't get to heaven?" Harry pressed his point. "You know the Bible better than I do, Parson. I have the distinct impression that I've read or heard this somewhere."

"You're referring to Paul's letters where he says that neither the immoral, nor idolators, nor adulterers, nor homosexuals, nor thieves, nor the greedy, nor the drunkards, nor revilers, nor robbers will inherit the kingdom of heaven." The parson's memory of scripture pirouetted before the group.

"That'll do," said Harry. "As far as I'm concerned that means most of us here either won't get much out of life now or won't be invited into heaven. Some of us will have fun and others will hope that a correction will take place after they die for being good little boys and girls."

"I guess Paul's easily misunderstood here," replied Parson McFright thoughtfully. "He doesn't mean we earn eternal life or God's love for us by being good, or for that matter doing something extraordinarily significant. We can't manipulate God into caring for us, any more than you can trick Harriet into loving you. Suppose every time you went on a hunting trip you tried to pacify Harriet by promising her a trip to South America or something like that."

"That might help," Harriet stage-whispered from the side.

"It might help if you enjoyed being with one another all the way to South America," said the Parson grimly. "But if Harry acts in such a way that he's never with you, never will be with your friends, and never shares your interests, then his hunting trips might well indicate either that he no longer is growing in love for you or that he doubts seriously your love for him."

"I've wondered about that, too," Harriet exclaimed, triggering a laugh from the group.

"Let him make his point, Harriet," Harry muttered.

"Well, the point is this," continued McFright, "the Corinthian Christians to whom Paul is writing had, so to speak, committed themselves to God's love and promise of love in

Jesus Christ, kind of like Harry and Harriet getting married
and pledging their mutual love and loyalty to each other.
But later they acted as if they didn't believe in their union
with God in Christ by the way they treated themselves and
their fellow man. Paul was really raising the question of
whether they still believed in God's love for them and for
other people or, if you will, if they still believed in their
own capacity to love and be loved as human beings. It
wasn't so much that they were breaking the commandments, but that they were being unfaithful to their com-
mitment to God's love for them and through them to others.
They were escaping the responsibility of love, and Paul
called them on it."

"They sound like normal human beings to me," countered
Harry. "I get so cotton-picking fed up at times that I either
want to run away from it all or get good and drunk, or
both."

"O.K.," said McFright, "it's obvious that Paul got dis-
couraged. My wife will tell you that I get so down that I
can't figure which way is up. But Paul is not accusing the
Corinthians, or implicitly you or me, of breaking the law.
He accuses them—and us—of losing faith in God's love for
us and God's power to love through us by what we do. The
Corinthian Christians were failing to grow in their capacity
for human love precisely because they couldn't be open and
honest with God and one another. They were dodging the
fact that they were not living up to their marriage vows to

Christ. I agree with you, Harry, that animals are open and honest in what they do. And I believe that we can be as open and honest to one another and to God the moment we honestly believe that God is interested in us, forgives us, and encourages us to love creatively and bravely. Frankly, if I didn't believe that, I'd be more of a hypocrite than I usually am."

"Say, Lillian, how about dinner?" Lillian's long-suffering husband had been listening from the sidelines, but his stomach was howling to get in on the party.

"All right," replied Lillian, "we can carry on our conversation in the dining room if you wish."

"Frankly I'd rather talk about baseball—or anything else," exclaimed her spouse. "And if it's all right with you, I'm going to keep the parson and Harry apart so I can digest my meal."

"Oh, you always spoil the fun. You can't stand a little healthy conflict, but I love you anyway." Lillian kissed her husband surreptitiously on the cheek.

"Come on, everyone—intermission time."

There was silence in the Cochrane car for some minutes after they left the Van der Water's party.

"Why didn't you tell me that the parson was going to be there?" muttered Harry as they paused for a stop light.

"You'd never have gone if I'd told you, and besides, I wanted to prove to you that all clergymen weren't 'mealy-mouthed.' "

"Well, I'm a little embarrassed about the conversation, now that I think about it. He didn't change my mind one bit, but I did admire the way he stood up for what he believes."

"Harry, what did you think about his suggestion of South America?"

"I knew that would come up again," said Harry glumly. "That parson doesn't know what he did to me with that remark. If I say it costs too much money or I haven't the time, you'll bring up my hunting. And if I say I'll be bored stiff, you'll say I don't love you anymore."

"Do you love me, Harry?" asked Harriet. "Do you think we're growing in love?"

The Author

The Rev. Allen Whitman is rector of St. George's Episcopal Church, St. Louis Park, Minn. He previously served churches at LaGrange, Ill., and St. Peter and LeCenter, Minn.

He has degrees from University of Minnesota, the University of Chicago Federated Theological Schools, and Northwestern Lutheran Theological Seminary, Minneapolis, Minn. He also studied analytical psychology at the C. G. Jung Institute in Zurich, Switzerland, and pursued further study on the mission of the church in the lives of people at Canterbury, England.

Mr. Whitman is an avid sports fan—particularly baseball, hockey, and football.